MY MAX BOOK!

If you should find my book, please return it to me (after you have had lots of fun reading it!).

NAME _____

STREET _____

CITY _____

STATE _____ ZIP _____

What travels all over the United States but stays in one corner? ANSWER: ¡dɯɐʇs∀

1

DEAR PARENTS,

Welcome to *Travels With MAX to the Supreme Court!* Endorsed by teachers and parents, this book reinforces the philosophy that "fun is learning and learning is fun." With the assistance of their guide, MAX, children tour the Supreme Court Building, interview the Chief Justice, solve puzzles and brain teasers, and attend a surprise party given by the nine Supreme Court Justices.

When the Supreme Court tour ends, the fun continues for kids. They are now eligible to join MAX's **VIK (Very Important Kid) Club.** As soon as children send MAX their Frequent Reader Coupon, he will mail them their VIK card. This card makes children official members of his club, and enables them to receive lots of MAX surprises. The Coupon and MAX's address can be found on page 47.

Giving *Travels With MAX* to children prior to visiting the Supreme Court is the perfect gift to prepare them for this exciting and educational trip. For children who are unable to visit the Supreme Court, receiving this book is the next best thing! If you would like to receive additional information regarding the Supreme Court, please feel free to contact the Supreme Court Historical Society at (202) 554-8300.

Travels With MAX to the Supreme Court is part of a series written on the three branches of government. The other two books within this series are entitled *Travels With MAX to the White House* and *Travels With MAX to the U.S. Capitol*. For information on these books and the other books that MAX has written, please feel free to call his hot line at **1-800-4-MAX-008**. Now, on with the tour!

Thank you for traveling with us,

Nancy Ann Van Wie

Nancy Ann Van Wie, M.Ed., and MAX!
Authors

A SUPREME THANK YOU!

MAX would like to thank the Supreme Court Historical Society for asking him to write the Supreme Court's first children's book, and for its support and assistance in preparing this book. MAX would also like to thank the teachers and students who helped him proofread and edit *Travels With MAX to the Supreme Court!*

ISBN 0-9626206-3-7
ALL RIGHTS RESERVED

ILLUSTRATORS: KARI MOE (COVER)
CHRISTINE URBIN (TEXT)

COPYRIGHT © 1994
PRINTED IN THE U.S.A.

LOOK INSIDE!

SUPREME COURT MANNERS!

Today you will visit the most famous Court in the United States - **the Supreme Court!** In preparation for your trip, MAX's court would like you to memorize the following Do's and Don'ts.

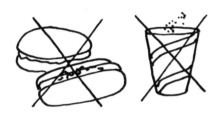

1. **DO NOT** bring food or drinks into the the Supreme Court Building. Also, do not run or yell in the building.

2. **DO** be polite. Say "please" and "thank you" when asking someone a question, and be patient while waiting in line.

3. **DO** have an awesome time! It is an honor and a privilege to visit the Supreme Court, and it is also lots of fun! Now, let the tour begin!

TRAVELS WITH MAX!

Good Day, Mate. My name is MAX! I am a **VIK** (**V**ery **I**mportant **K**oala) who writes children's travel books. As a well-known author, I have famous friends all over the world. Today I am traveling to Washington, D.C., to visit nine famous friends. They are the Supreme Court Justices. My friends work for the **highest** court in the nation - the **Supreme Court of the United States**. Would you like to travel with me to Washington, D.C., to meet the Supreme Court Justices? Then climb aboard, Mate!

IT'S FUN TIME!

Welcome aboard the Supreme Court Express! We at VIK Tours will do everything we can to make your trip fun! There will be games and puzzles to solve, brain teasers to test your memory, and lots of pictures to color.

When you return home, you can join MAX's **VIK** (**V**ery **I**mportant **K**id) Club. To become a member, mail the Frequent Reader Coupon. It's on page 47. Now, sit back and relax!

Before we take off, can you find the 8 hidden objects below? Good luck!

 flag   law book   pencil   inkwell   star   quill pen   gavel   eagle   **7**

HERE WE GO!

We are now in the air, cruising at an altitude of 32,000 feet. As we fly over the United States, **connect the dots** to complete my map. Can you find Washington, D.C.? This famous city is the capital of the United States. Here is where the President lives and works, where Congress makes laws, and where the **Supreme Court** is located.

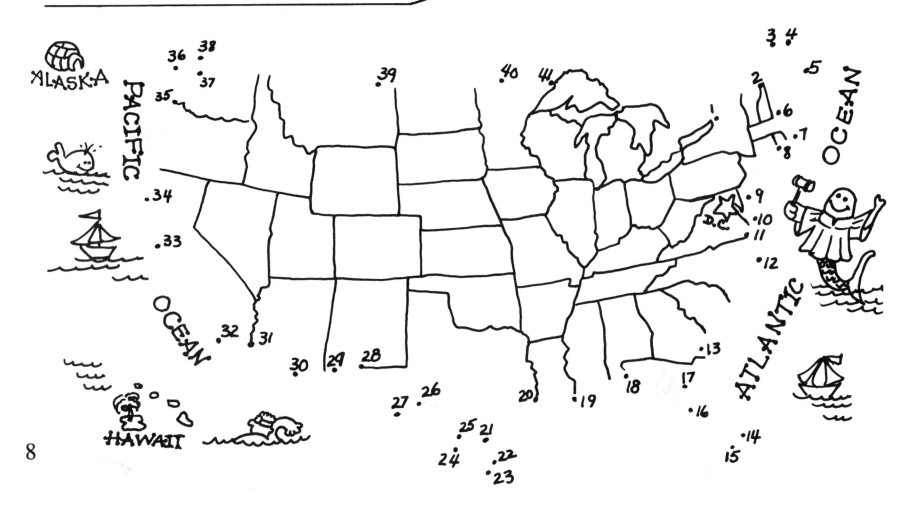

A SUPREME MOVIE!

Our flying time to Washington, D.C., will be four hours and ten minutes. On this flight you will receive a complimentary meal and movie. While you enjoy courtburgers, supreme fries and milk, you can watch today's film, "The Story of the Supreme Court." The movie starts in one minute, so put on your headphones, munch on your meal, and have fun!

In the 1600s, England began setting up colonies along the eastern coast of North America. By the 1700s, 13 colonies were established. During this time the colonies had to pay taxes to the King of England. When the King demanded more taxes, the 13 colonies decided they no longer wanted to be ruled by England. The colonies rebelled, and in 1775 war broke out. This was the start of the American Revolution. On July 4, 1776, the United States was born when the 13 colonies signed the **Declaration of Independence.** It declared the 13 colonies free and independent of England.

Can you find the 8 words hidden in my puzzle?

UNITED   REBEL   ENGLAND   TAX   COLONIST

KING

FREE

RULE

C	O	L	O	N	I	S	T
F	R	E	B	E	L	J	A
R	U	N	I	T	E	D	X
E	L	M	K	I	N	G	O
E	E	N	G	L	A	N	D

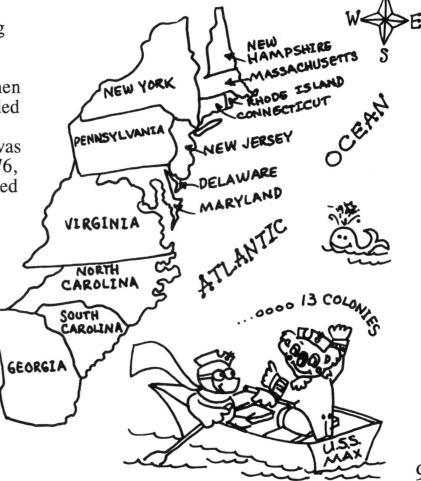

9

THE CONSTITUTION!

In 1783, seven years after signing the Declaration of Independence, the Americans won the Revolution. Now, who would rule this new nation? In 1787 a group of **delegates** (people chosen to act for others) answered that question by writing the Constitution of the United States. The **Constitution** is a plan of government. It states the basic laws and principles that guide this great nation's government.

The delegates did not want their government to be ruled by one person, such as a king. They wanted their government to have what they called "separation of powers" and "checks and balances." So the Constitution provided for **three branches of government**. Each branch could check on one another, so that no one branch could have too much power. These three branches of government are the **legislative branch** (represented by the United States Congress), **executive branch** (represented by the President of the United States), and the **judicial branch** (represented by the Supreme Court of the United States).

Below are 8 words that are mentioned in the Constitution. Can you put them in alphabetical order?

HISTORY   BRANCHES   EXECUTIVE   AMERICA   JUDICIAL   LAWS   GOVERNMENT   LEGISLATIVE

1. _____

2. _____

3. _____

4. _____

5. _____

6. _____

7. _____

8. _____

10

THE CONSTITUTION SAYS ...

What did the delegates want the Supreme Court to do?
The delegates wanted the Supreme Court to interpret (to explain) the Constitution, which is the supreme law of the land. They also wanted the Supreme Court to check on the Congress and the President to make sure that neither branch of government received too much power.

Who would appoint the Supreme Court Justices?
The delegates decided that the President of the United States would appoint (choose) the Justices with the advice and consent (agreement) of the Senate. Unlike the President, who is elected every four years, Justices serve on good behavior or until they choose to retire.

Follow the picture clues to see who was the President who appointed the first Supreme Court Justices!

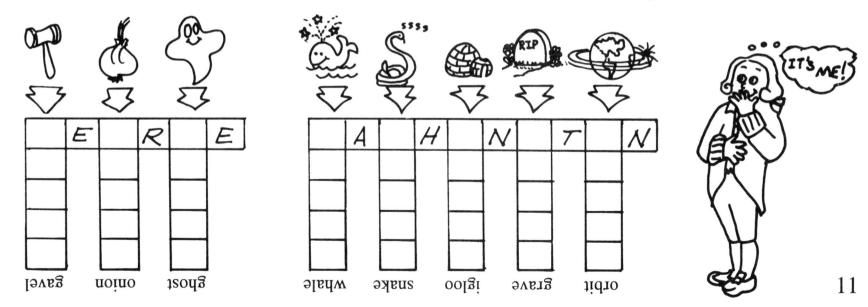

	E		R		E

gavel · onion · ghost

	A		H		N		T		N

whale · snake · igloo · grave · orbit

THE FIRST CHIEF JUSTICE!

That's right, Mate! **George Washington**, the first President of the United States, had the honor of choosing the nation's first Supreme Court Justices. The first Court had only six Justices: a Chief Justice and five Associate Justices. Today, the Supreme Court has nine Justices: a Chief Justice and eight Associate Justices.

Who was the Supreme Court's first Chief Justice? Decode my puzzle to find out.

A) Fill in the missing letter for each box. **B)** Do the math problems. **C)** Match the number from Box B to the number in Box A. Now take the underlined letter from Box A and place it in Box C, under the math answer.

A.

1. M _ ON	2. _ELLY	3. SK _	4. HE _ RT		5. S _ OE	6. _EWEL	7. HA _ D

B.

21 − 19	100 − 99	63 − 58	42 − 35		280 − 274	89 − 85	72 − 69

C.

__	__	__	__		__	__	__

THE COURT'S FIRST HOME!

Right again! Now that you know that **John Jay** was the first Chief Justice, let's learn where the Supreme Court held its first meeting. On February 1, 1790, the first Supreme Court met in the Merchants Exchange Building located in New York City, then the seat of the government. The Supreme Court met in one room on the second floor of the Merchants Exchange Building, and on the ground floor there was an open-air market.

Here is the Merchants Exchange Building where the first Court met. Can you find the 8 hidden objects?

carrot   paper clip   cheese   book   candle   arrow   cupcake   comb

THE COURT TRAVELS TO...

The Supreme Court was located in New York for just one year. In 1791 the government, including the Supreme Court, moved to Philadelphia, the nation's capital until 1800. The Supreme Court remained in Philadelphia until 1800 and then it relocated to Washington, D.C., now the nation's capital. For the next 135 years (1800 to 1935), the Court was located in several rooms throughout the Capitol Building. The Capitol Building is where Congress (the legislative branch) meets. In 1935 a separate building was built for the Supreme Court, which is located across from the Capitol Building. Today millions of people from all over the world visit the famous Supreme Court Building.

Follow the route that the Supreme Court traveled from New York to Philadelphia to Washington, D.C.

14

A SUPREME QUIZ!

Well Mate, that's the end of the movie. I hope you enjoyed it. I also hope you were paying attention, because now you have to take a **quiz**. Circle the answer that you think is correct. When you finish, turn to the page listed to see how you did.
No peeking allowed! Good luck and have fun!

1. In the 1600s England started setting up colonies along the eastern coast of:
   Australia   OR   the North Pole   OR   North America   (Page   9)

2. The document that declared the 13 colonies free and independent of England was:
   the Declaration of Independence   OR   the Constitution of the United States   (Page   9)

3. The Constitution of the United States is a plan of government that provided for:
   7 branches of government   OR   3 branches of government   (Page 10)

4. The 3 branches of government are represented by the President, the Congress and:
   the King of England   OR   the Supreme Court   (Page 10)

5. In 1790 the first Supreme Court met in the Merchants Exchange Building in:
   Paris, France   OR   New York City, New York   OR   Rome, Italy   (Page 13)

6. The first Supreme Court had 6 Justices. Today, the Supreme Court has:
   9 Justices   OR   10 Justices   OR   11 Justices   (Page 12)

7. The Supreme Court Building is located in the nation's capital. That city is:
   Hollywood, California   OR   Washington, D.C.   (Page 14)

Good job, Mate. You are so smart! Now, fasten your seat belt. We will be on the ground in 5 minutes.   15

HURRAH, WE'RE HERE!

Welcome to Washington, D.C., the nation's capital! Soon we will be at the Supreme Court. As we travel there, we will pass the White House and the Capitol Building. Are you ready? Here we go!

Oops! My driver forgot his directions. Can you help him find the way to the Supreme Court Building?

AWESOME BUILDING!

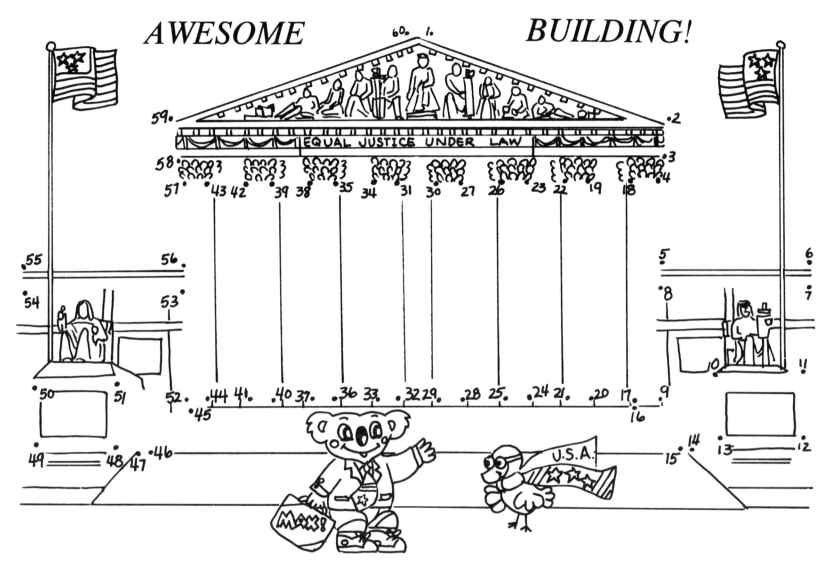

We're here! Connect the dots to see the **Supreme Court Building!** Made out of marble, it's awesome looking. As you walk up the steps, you will see two huge statues. The female statue on the left represents Contemplation of Justice; the male statue on the right represents the Authority of Law. At the top of the steps you will see 16 columns. Over them is written: **"Equal Justice Under Law."** These words express the responsibility of the Supreme Court, which is to interpret the law fairly according to the Constitution of the United States. Are you ready to go inside? Follow me, Mate!

LET THE TOUR BEGIN!

Now that we are inside the Supreme Court Building, what are we going to do? My Tour Director just handed me the schedule. From 11 a.m. to 12 noon, we will tour the Supreme Court Building. At 12:15 p.m. I will interview the Chief Justice. Then at 3 p.m. we will have our picture taken with the nine Supreme Court Justices. This is an awesome schedule!

Before we start our tour, our personal items need to be inspected by the Supreme Court police officers. I hope you remembered that no food or drinks may be brought into this building. Follow me, Mate!

Hold it! The police officers see food and drinks. You can't enter until you find the 9 hidden objects.

18   milk carton   hot dog   banana   cake   donut   apple   lemon slice   grapes   soda can

CHIEF JUSTICE JOHN MARSHALL!

Welcome to the ground floor where you will see several neat exhibits. There is a huge bronze statue of a famous Chief Justice named **John Marshall**. In 1801, President John Adams, the second President of the United States, chose John Marshall as the Chief Justice. Chief Justice Marshall served on the Court for 34 years. Because of his influence on the Court, he is often called "**the great Chief Justice.**"

Connect the dots to see the bronze statue of Chief Justice John Marshall.

A COOL STAIRCASE!

Also on the ground floor you will see two famous **spiral staircases**! Here is one of them. Isn't it cool?

Can you find me? I am on the ground floor looking upppp, and my assistant, Birdie, is on the top floor looking downnnn.

Years ago, you could walk up the 136 steps that take you from the basement floor to the third floor. But today, the spiral staircases are closed to the public.

There are only a few spiral staircases like this one in the entire world! Two are in the Supreme Court Building; one is in the Paris Opera House in Paris, France; one is in the Vatican in Vatican City, Italy, where the Pope lives; and one is in the Minnesota State Capitol Building.

If you think this is cool, wait until you find out what else there is to see and do in the Supreme Court Building. Follow us!

A SURPRISE FOR YOU!

There's lots more to do on this floor! You can stop by the Theatre to watch a free movie that describes the Court; if you're hungry there is a snack bar and a cafeteria; and if you want to buy some neat books and gifts, you can visit the Supreme Court Historical Society Gift Shop. When you go into the gift shop say, **"MAX sent me"** and my pals will give you a …

To find out what you will receive, **do the following**: A) Spell the missing words by putting the correct letters in the spaces. B) Use those same letters to fill in the spaces at the bottom that have matching numbers. (If you need help, reread the page listed at the end of each sentence.)

1. The Supreme Court is the highest ___ ___ ___ ___ ___ in the land! (Page 6)
    1 2 3 4 5

2. George Washington was the first ___ ___ ___ ___ ___ ___ ___ ___ ___ of the U.S. (Page 12)
    6 7 8 9 10 11 12 13 14

3. President Washington chose the first ___ ___ ___ ___ ___ ___ ___ Court Justices. (Page 12)
    15 16 17 18 19 20 21

4. John Jay was the first Chief ___ ___ ___ ___ ___ ___ ___ of the Supreme Court. (Page 13)
    22 23 24 25 26 27 28

5. John ___ ___ ___ ___ ___ ___ ___ ___ has been called "the Great Chief Justice." (Page 19)
    29 30 31 32 33 34 35 36

___ ___ ___ ___ ___ ___ ___   ___ ___ ___ ___ ___   ___ ___ ___ ___ ___ ___ ___ ___ !
9 3 17 31 28 20 12   27 2 23 7 14   32 16 4 6 18 26 15 8

A SUPREME HAIR CUT!

Before we leave the ground floor and go upstairs to tour the Great Hall and the Courtroom, I need to stop by the barber shop for a little trim.

The barber shop? That's right, Mate. Most people do not know that there is a Supreme Court Barber Shop. But there is, and it's open to the public! The Supreme Court barber is a good guy. He's a good barber, too. If you need your hair cut, be sure to make an appointment far ahead because he's very busy.

Now that I'm looking totally awesome after my supreme cut, let's find our way to the Great Hall.

WELCOME TO THE GREAT HALL!

This is the **Great Hall!** In this room you will see marble busts of the former Chief Justices who have served on the Court since President Washington appointed John Jay, the first Chief Justice. As you look around, see if you can find the bust of Chief Justice William Howard Taft. Before **Chief Justice Taft** was appointed to the Court, he served as the twenty-seventh President of the United States. He is the only person in history to hold both offices! He is well-known for another accomplishment, too. It was his idea for the Supreme Court to have its own building, but he never saw his dream come true. He died before the building was completed. Now, let's look at the busts before we tour the Courtroom.

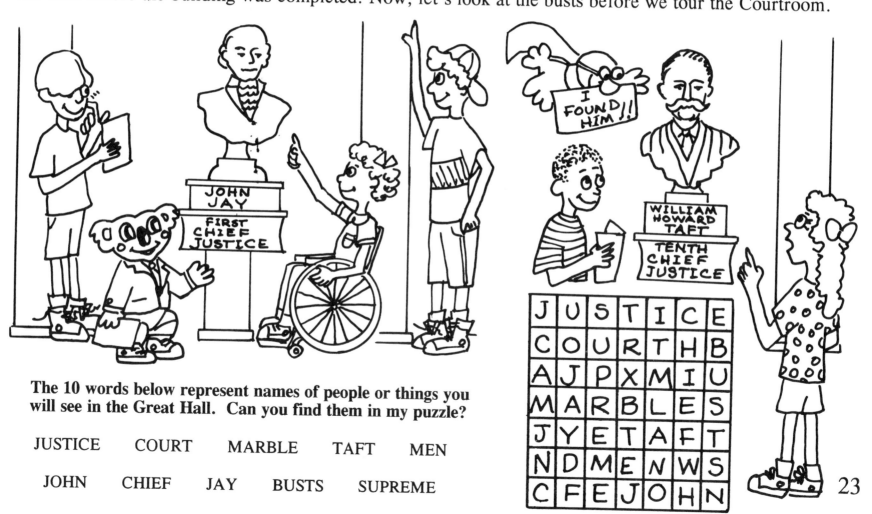

The 10 words below represent names of people or things you will see in the Great Hall. Can you find them in my puzzle?

JUSTICE   COURT   MARBLE   TAFT   MEN

JOHN   CHIEF   JAY   BUSTS   SUPREME

23

THE MOST FAMOUS COURTROOM!

Welcome to the Courtroom! Here is the Bench where the nine Supreme Court Justices sit. The Chief Justice sits in the center and the eight Associate Justices are seated to the Chief's right and left, in order of seniority. The Bench is curved so that the Justices can see and hear one another.

When Court is in session, children are allowed in the Courtroom, although there are rules that children (and adults) must obey. No writing, sketching or whispering is allowed in the Courtroom.

ALL RISE, COURT IS IN SESSION!

I have an idea! Let's pretend that Court is in session today and that I am the Chief Justice and eight of my friends are the Associate Justices. Shortly before 10 a.m., a buzzer will signal the nine Justices to the Robing Room where they will put on their robes and shake hands with one another. Then, exactly at 10 o'clock, the **Marshal** (the person who announces the arrival of the Justices) brings down his gavel, and everyone rises as he says:

"The Honorable, the Chief Justice and the Associate Justices of the Supreme Court of the United States." As the Marshal says this, the Justices enter and stand in front of their chairs. Then the Marshal says: "**Oyez!** (Pronounced o-yay, it means hear-ye.) **Oyez! Oyez!** All persons having business before the Honorable, the Supreme Court of the United States, are admonished to draw near and give their attention, for the Court is now sitting. God save the United States and this Honorable Court!"

Then the Marshal brings down the gavel again, and the Justices and everyone else sit down.

The vacant chair is for you to sit in. Today, you are an Associate Justice. Draw yourself next to me!   25

THE JUSTICES LISTEN AND THINK!

Court is now in session! The Supreme Court Justices will hear the first case. Each case is one hour and each lawyer has thirty minutes to present his or her side of the case. To present their cases, lawyers stand behind a lectern that holds their notes. On the lectern there are two microphones. Between the microphones are two lights that the lawyers need to watch: One light is white; the other is red. When the white light glows, the lawyer has only five minutes left to argue the case. When the red light glows, the lawyer's time is up.

Use the picture clues to spell what the Justices see in the Courtroom.

THE JUSTICES DECIDE!

Two times a week, when Court is in session, the Justices meet in a private conference to discuss and decide the cases they heard in Court. Five minutes before conference time, a buzzer signals the Supreme Court Justices to their Conference Room.

All conferences are **"top secret!"** Only the Justices are allowed inside their Conference Room. To make sure that no one enters, the junior Associate Justice acts as "doorkeeper."

When the Justices enter the room, they shake hands with one another. Then the Chief Justice, who sits at the head of the table, announces the first case to be discussed. After discussing the case, the Justices vote on the case. After a decision has been made, one of the Justices writes an **opinion** for the Court. An opinion is a document that states the decision of the Justices.

THE OPINION IS READY!

After an opinion has been written and reviewed, final copies go to the Clerk for safekeeping and also to the Reporter of Decisions. An opinion can be several pages long, so the Reporter writes a "headnote" (short report) of the decision. The headnote helps the press (the people who report the news) to relay the news faster.

Once the Reporter has written the headnote, the Supreme Court is ready to announce its decision to the public. Within seconds of the announcement, the Clerk's office calls the Information Officer to release the opinion. Then copies of the opinion are distributed to the press.

The Information Officer gives copies of the opinion to the public and to the press who are eager to ...

What are they eager to do?
To solve the mystery, decode my math puzzle by doing the following:

32	11	95	76	24	36	94	42	58
+ 33	+ 22	+ 13	+17	+16	+21	+69	+ 44	+ 21
R	E	J	P	A	O	R	M	T

A. Solve the math problems.
B. Circle the letters with the odd-numbered math answers.
C. Starting with the first circled letter, fill in the blanks.

42	81	96	77	83	54	29	65	48
- 29	- 17	- 35	- 66	- 44	- 28	- 10	-18	- 23
T	X	H	E	N	V	E	W	S

28   **They are eager to**   __ __ __ __ __ __ __ __ __   __ __ __ __

SUPREME BRAIN TEASERS!

Well Mate, there you have it! I hope my Courtroom tour helped you to understand how the Supreme Court Justices hear and decide cases. Now before we meet my friend, the Chief Justice, let's see how much you remember. Here are my **Supreme Brain Teasers!** You had better put on your thinking cap for this quiz. Read the question carefully, then circle your answer. When you finish, turn to the page listed to see how you did. No peeking allowed! Have fun!

1. The awesome looking Supreme Court Building is made out of:
   gold   OR   marble   OR   silver   OR   copper   (Page 17)

2. In the Great Hall, you can see marble busts of the former:
   Presidents of the United States   OR   Chief Justices of the United States   (Page 23)

3. When the Justices are seated at the Supreme Court Bench, the Chief Justice sits:
   on the right end   OR   in the center   OR   on the left end   (Page 24)

4. The Justices can see and hear one another in the Courtroom because the Bench is:
   square   OR   round   OR   oblong   OR   curved   (Page 24)

5. When lawyers present their case to the Supreme Court, each lawyer has only:
   30 minutes to present his or her case   OR   30 hours to present his or her case   (Page 26)

6. When the Justices meet in their Conference Room to discuss cases, these conferences are:
   open to the public   OR   Top Secret! No one is allowed inside   (Page 27)

Awesome work! You get an A+. Now, since you did such a good job, do you think you can help me do the crossword puzzle that the Chief Justice sent me? It's on the next page. Thanks, Mate!

THE CHIEF JUSTICE'S PUZZLE!

The Chief Justice is so smart! He told me that from the two words, **SUPREME COURT**, he made 45 other words. Here is his puzzle, using 18 of those words. To solve it, **this is what you do**. Use the clues below to fill in the boxes on the next page. If you don't know an answer that's okay. Go on to the next question. As you fill in the boxes with the correct letters, those letters will help you solve the rest of the puzzle. Good luck, Mate, and thanks for your help!

ACROSS

1. Golfers set their ball on top of a __ __ __ .

2. Eyes let us __ __ __ .

3. The opposite of go is __ __ __ __ . (Rhymes with some)

4. The opposite of less is __ __ __ __ __ . (Rhymes with store)

5. You boil water in a __ __ __ . (Rhymes with lot.)

6. A leopard has black __ __ __ __ __ __ on its coat.

7. Dogs and cats are good __ __ __ __ __ .

8. When something hurts, it's __ __ __ __ __ . (Rhymes with more)

9. Another name for policeman is __ __ __ __ .

DOWN

1. In autumn, leaves fall off a __ __ __ __ .

2. Stairs have many __ __ __ __ __ __ .

3. The recipe calls for 2 __ __ __ __ __ of sugar.

4. She washed the floor with 2 __ __ __ __ __ .

5. Today, we are on a VIK __ __ __ __ __ .

6. __ __ __ __ __ the milk. (Rhymes with four)

7. Another name for pocketbook is __ __ __ __ __ __ __ .

8. Chicken __ __ __ __ __ is good for a cold.

9. We use scissors to __ __ __ .

30

THIS IS A COOL COURT PUZZLE!

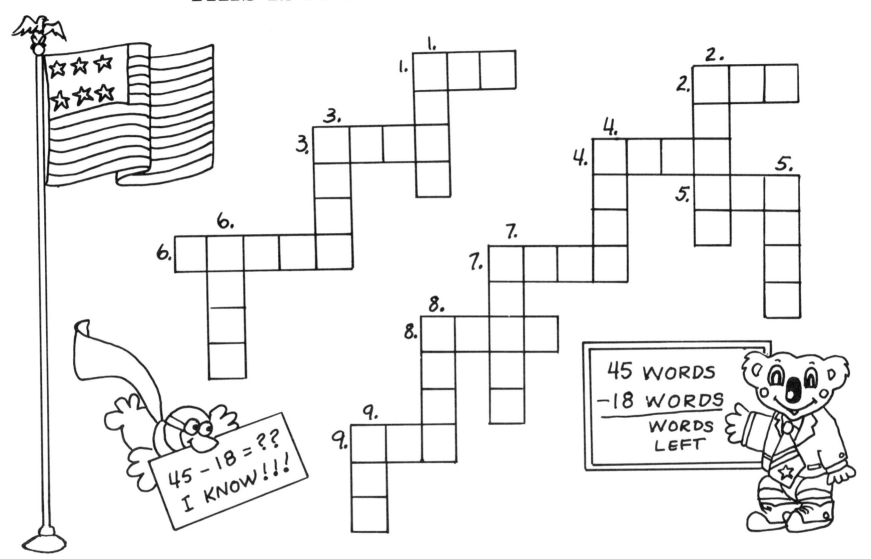

From the two words **SUPREME COURT**, the Chief Justice made 45 other words. You just solved 18 of them. There are 27 words left. They are: **stump, stomp, route, spout, romp, prom, emperor, sort, port, crop, sure, me, so, out, super, top, cot, meet, put, rot, met, up, our, core, tore, seem, stop.**

Can you make more words? If you can, mail them to me and I'll send you a prize for being so smart!

31

A VERY IMPORTANT PERSON!

Thanks Mate, for helping me do the Supreme Court puzzle. Now we are ready to meet the Chief Justice. The Chief Justice is a very important person. His formal title is The Chief Justice of the United States!

The Chief Justice has a very important and busy job. He has many duties to perform. Three of his duties are: (1) to preside over the Court, (2) to preside over the Justices' secret conferences, and (3) to preside over the judiciary (joo-dish-e-er-e), all of the courts in the land.

As busy as the Chief Justice is, he always has time for his friends. Today he is taking time out of his busy schedule so I can interview him for my book. What a guy!

Are you ready to meet The Chief Justice of the United States? Then follow me, Mate!

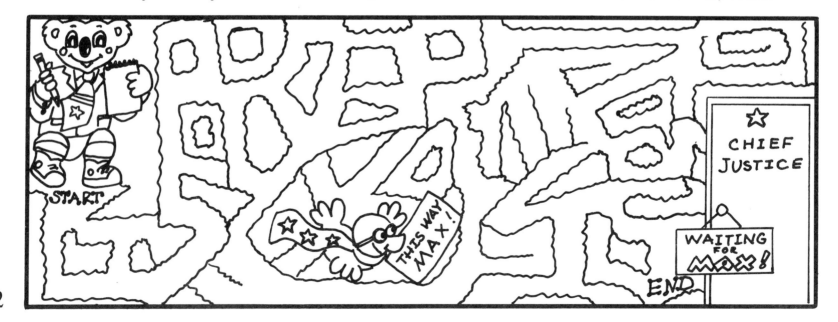

MY FRIEND, THE CHIEF JUSTICE!

I am now sitting with the Chief Justice of the United States! This is such a privilege and an honor. I thanked the Chief Justice for taking the time to meet with me.

"MAX, that is what friends are for," the Chief Justice replied. Then he congratulated me on my exciting career as a successful author, and said he thought it was a great idea that I was writing a children's book about the Supreme Court.

I told him I had lots of questions that kids wanted answered by only the Chief Justice. With a big smile the Chief Justice remarked, "Smart kids!"

Write down 3 things you would like to ask the Chief Justice!

1. _____

   _____

2. _____

   _____

3. _____

   _____

Turn the page to read my interview with the Chief Justice of the United States!

33

MAX'S INTERVIEW!

Here is my interview with the Chief Justice
of the United States!

MAX: **Mr. Chief Justice, why do the Supreme Court Justices wear black robes while in Court?**

Chief Justice: Great question, MAX! Wearing black robes while in Court is a **tradition** that the Supreme Court Justices have been honoring for almost 200 years. The black robes that the Justices wear are similar to those worn by early colonial judges.

MAX, another tradition is when the Justices **shake hands** with one another before Court and also at the beginning of their conferences. This tradition was started more than 100 years ago by Chief Justice Melville Fuller.

The **quill pen** is also a tradition that is still honored in the Courtroom. White feather pens called quill pens are placed on the lawyers' tables each day before Court, even though no one uses them anymore. At the end of Court, lawyers are allowed to keep the quill pens as souvenirs.

THE LONG, BUMPY ROAD!

MAX: Is there anything that the first Justices had to do that today's Justices do not have to do?

Chief Justice: Boy, did they! It's called **Circuit Riding**. In 1790, Congress required the first Justices to travel two times a year to distant places to preside over district courts called circuit (sur-kit) courts. The Justices traveled by stagecoach from city to city. The long, bumpy rides were so uncomfortable that the first Chief Justice, John Jay, almost resigned. After three years of the Justices' complaining, Congress decided they had to travel only one time a year. Circuit riding did not end until 1891.

Below are 6 states to which the Justices often traveled. Can you put them in alphabetical order?

PENNSYLVANIA   VIRGINIA   MARYLAND   NEW YORK   GEORGIA   DELAWARE

1. _____

2. _____

3. _____

4. _____

5. _____

6. _____

35

THE JURY HAS REACHED A VERDICT!

MAX: **Mr. Chief Justice, how does a case reach the Supreme Court?**

Chief Justice: Outstanding question! Here's the answer, MAX. Before a case reaches the Supreme Court, the highest Court in the land, it first has to be heard by many **lower courts**. Lower courts usually have one judge and a jury, and a jury is usually made up of 12 citizens. After the lawyers for each side have argued their case, the jury makes a final decision called the **verdict**.

The jury has reached a verdict. Before the judge reads it, can you find the 10 hidden objects below?

mushroom   fork   heart   toothbrush   cup   knife   snake   light bulb   scissors   stars

I APPEAL! ON TO THE SUPREME COURT!

Chief Justice: Now MAX, once the verdict has been read, if either side is unhappy with it, the case can be appealed. When a case is **appealed**, it is taken to a higher court to have that court give its opinion on whether the verdict was right or wrong.

In an appeal case there are no juries or witnesses. Instead of one judge, there can be three, five, seven or nine judges, depending on how high the court is. After the lawyers for both sides have given their arguments, the judges give their **opinion** on the verdict.

Depending on that court's opinion, lawyers may appeal the case again to a higher court. This can keep going until a case reaches the Supreme Court. But not all cases reach the Supreme Court. Each year about 6,000 cases are appealed to the Supreme Court, and only 120 - 150 of those cases are accepted.

Let's pretend you are a lawyer who wants to appeal a case. First, you have to find the 9 hidden words.

HIGHER   LAW   APPEAL   RIGHT   OPINION   LOWER   COURTS   CASE   WRONG

C	A	S	E	H	J	B	L
O	P	I	N	I	O	N	O
U	P	R	I	G	H	T	W
R	E	V	W	H	X	A	E
T	A	A	M	E	J	C	R
S	L	X	W	R	O	N	G

A VERY IMPORTANT CASE!

MAX: **Mr. Chief Justice, have there been any Supreme Court cases that involved children's rights?**

Chief Justice: Yes, MAX. One case involved children, education, and the **Fourteenth Amendment** of the Constitution. An amendment is an addition to the Constitution. Today there are twenty-seven amendments to the Constitution. The Fourteenth Amendment provides for equal protection of the laws. In 1954 the Supreme Court heard a case that involved this amendment. Here is that case.

Many years ago, schools were "segregated." This meant that black children were "set apart" from white children. Black children attended one school; white children attended another school. But in 1954 when a black child named Linda Brown was turned away from an all-white school, her father said that her rights under the Fourteenth Amendment were violated. **The Supreme Court agreed!** Today, schools are no longer segregated. This case, *Brown versus Board of Education*, is one of the most famous cases in modern Court history.

MORE COURT FACTS!

MAX: Mr. Chief Justice, when is Court in session?

Chief Justice: Court begins the first Monday in October and usually ends in late June. During those months, Court is in session Monday through Wednesday for two weeks each month through April. The next two weeks the Justices review upcoming cases, write opinions on cases they have heard, and attend to other Court business.

MAX: Mr. Chief Justice, here is my last question. Could you please tell me when the first woman was appointed to serve on the Supreme Court?

Chief Justice: My pleasure, MAX. In 1789, President Washington appointed the first Supreme Court Justices, who were all men. Not until 1981, 192 years later, was the first woman appointed to serve on the Supreme Court! Then in 1993, the second woman was appointed to serve on the Supreme Court.

Use the picture clues to spell the name of the first woman Supreme Court Justice, appointed in 1981!

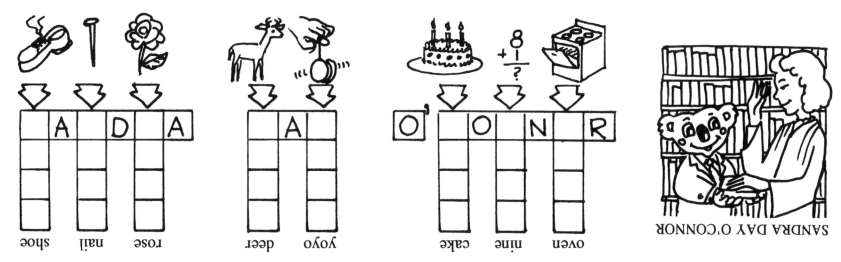

shoe   nail   rose   deer   yoyo   cake   nine   oven

SANDRA DAY O'CONNOR

A SPECIAL TOUR FOR MAX!

Wow! That was an awesome interview. After I thanked the Chief Justice, he said, "MAX, I have a surprise for you. At 3 p.m. I am having my picture taken with the eight Associate Justices and I want you to join us. But first, let's take a VIK tour of three rooms that are not open to the public. Three rooms that only special people, like you, may enter."

Then the Chief Justice said, "The first room we will visit is on the top floor, two floors above the Courtroom. Some people joke about this room being the highest court in the land. Follow me, MAX!"

Listen Mate, don't tell the Chief Justice this but I think he has been working too hard. After all, we all know that the Supreme Court is the **highest** Court in the land. So what court could be on the top floor?

Follow the maze to see where the Chief Justice is taking us. Have fun and good luck!

40

A FUN COURT!

YESSSS...

The Chief Justice is so cool. He was talking about the Supreme Court basketball court! The Chief Justice challenged me to a foul shot contest. He said that if I won, he would treat me to lunch. Well Mate, he forgot that I was on the Australian All-Star Basketball Team. Yesss! You guessed it, I won!

Where is the Chief Justice taking me for lunch? To solve the mystery, decode my math puzzle by doing the following:

45	10	48	53	32	79	27
+26	+18	+32	+16	+46	+13	+17
X	D	I	J	N	I	N

A. Solve the math problems.

B. Circle the letters with the even-numbered math answers.

57	91	63	84	76	39	82
- 31	- 48	- 45	- 52	- 69	- 17	- 64
G	E	R	O	A	O	M

C. Starting with the first circled letter, fill in the blanks.

We will have lunch in the Supreme Court __ __ __ __ __ __ __   __ __ __ __

41

MAX'S SUPREME MEAL!

This is the **Supreme Court Justices' Dining Room**! This beautiful room is used only by the Supreme Court Justices. As the Chief Justice and I enjoyed a delicious meal, he told me about the next room that we will visit on our VIK tour.

What room will we visit next? You will have to decode my puzzle to find out. This is what you do:

A) Fill in the missing letter for each box. **B)** Do the math problems. **C)** Match the number from Box B to the number in Box A. Now take the underlined letter from Box A and place it in Box C, under the math answer.

A.

1. COM_	2. F_OG	3. BI_D	4. _ION	5. KE_	6. R_IN	7. F_SH

B.

1.	2.	3.	4.	5.	6.	7.
191 −187	50 −43	301 −300	29 −27	174 −168	381 −378	62 −57

C.

__	__	__	__	__	__	__

THE SUPREME COURT LIBRARY!

Shhhh, we are now in the **Supreme Court Library**! The Chief Justice told me that there are more than 450,000 law books, records, and journals in this library.

He also told me that when the Justices start to write their opinion on a case, a lot of research is needed. Each Justice can have up to four law clerks who assist him or her. The law clerks research most of the information in this library. If they cannot find something, the librarian helps them.

Here are 14 things you will see in the Supreme Court Library. Can you help me find them in my puzzle? Thanks, Mate!

L	I	B	R	A	R	I	A	N
A	J	U	S	T	I	C	E	S
W	O	C	L	E	R	K	S	D
Y	U	H	I	R	U	G	X	E
E	R	A	G	B	O	O	K	S
R	N	I	H	P	E	N	S	K
S	A	R	T	A	B	L	E	S
X	L	S	S	L	A	M	P	S
M	S	R	E	C	O	R	D	S

LAWYERS   DESKS   LIBRARIAN   RECORDS   JOURNALS

CHAIRS   BOOKS   JUSTICES   CLERKS   LAMPS   RUG   TABLES   PENS   LIGHTS

IT'S SURPRISE TIME!

Well Mate, after visiting the library, the Chief Justice smiled and said, "MAX, are you ready to have your picture taken? In five minutes I will be meeting the eight Associate Justices for a Supreme Court photograph. Of course the Justices will be expecting me, but they won't be expecting you, too. Boy, will they be surprised! I can't wait to see the expressions on their faces. As soon as I put on my Justice's robe, we will be on our way."

Okay Mate, before I surprise the Associate Justices, let's see how many words you can make by using the word JUSTICES. I made 10. **Here are my clues**. Can you make more words? Good luck!

JUSTICES

1. — — —

2.  — — —

3.  — — —

4. __ __ __
   S T E

5. __ __ __
   S E U

6. __ __ __
   J T U

7. __ __
   T I

8. __ __ __ __
   S J T U

9.  — — —

10. 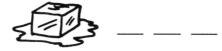 — — — —

44 **ANSWERS:** 1. tie 2. ice 3. jet 4. set 5. sue (or use) 6. jut 7. it 8. just 9. sit 10. suit

A SUPREME SURPRISE PARTY!

Shhhh, we don't want the Associate Justices to know that I am out here. The Chief Justice just went inside the East Conference Room. He told me to wait two minutes, then enter and say, "Surprise!" This is going be so much fun. Let's see, two minutes are up. Here I go, Mate.

"Surprise, MAX! Surprise!" the Justices shouted.

"MAX," the Chief Justice said, "are you confused? This surprise party is for you! It is our way of saying 'thank you' for writing a children's book on the Supreme Court. Don't forget, we want lots of autographed books. Now, let's take that group picture you were expecting. Smile, MAX!"

When the party ended, I hugged everybody good-bye and promised to send them lots of autographed books. As I left the building, I thought: **I know why Americans are proud of the Supreme Court!** 45

MY TRAVEL DIARY!

Well Mate, our VIK tour is over and it's time for us to return home. I hope you had lots of fun. I know I did! While I am flying you home, **write and draw** in your travel diary about the neat things we did on our Supreme Court tour!

Dear Diary,

Today is _____ .

Fun rooms I visited _____

_____

_____ .

What I liked best _____

_____ .

_____ .

Draw 'n Color

What I Liked Best!

☆ *MAX'S VIK CLUB!*

Well Mate, now that you are home, it's time for me to refuel and return to Australia. On my way home, I'll stop off in California to visit my agent and to pick up my mail. I hope that your **Frequent Reader Coupon** will be there. As soon as I receive it, I will mail you your **VIK card**, which will make you an official member of my VIK Club!

When you return your Coupon, let me know what you liked best about this book. Also, please send me some silly riddles. Good-bye, Mate!

Your friend,

MAX
23015 Del Lago Drive
Suite D2-172
Laguna Hills, California 92653

FREQUENT READER COUPON

Hurry! Mail today to receive your **VIK card!**

I traveled with MAX to _____

My name is _____ Age _____ Grade _____

Address (Street) _____

City _____ State _____ Zip _____